thelonious monk

STRAIGHT NO CHASER

PIANO
ARRANGEMENTS

CHORD
SYMBOLS

FULLY TRANSCRIBED
SOLOS

Wise Publications

London / New York / Paris / Sydney / Copenhagen / Madrid

blue monk 8

brilliant corners 10

criss cross 12

evidence 16

hackensack 26

i mean you 20

in walked bud 22

little rootie tootie 30

misterioso 19

monk's dream 32

monk's mood 36

nutty 42

pannonica 46

rhythm-a-ning 39

round midnight 44

skippy 50

something in blue 48

straight no chaser 53

teo 56

thelonious 60

well you needn't 68

introduction 4

discography 72

introduction:

Few musicians in the history of jazz have had as great an impact as Thelonious Monk. As the 'father' of the be-bop movement in the 1940s, he is probably one of the most individual and influential jazz musicians. His numerous compositions have become timeless and his piano style has remained unique.

Thelonious Sphere Monk was born in Rocky Mount, North Carolina on 11th October 1917. His family moved to New York when he was five. He started piano lessons when he was eleven and by the time he was thirteen he was playing at local 'rent' parties in Harlem, as well as accompanying his mother on the organ at their local church.

After briefly studying at the Juilliard School, he started playing with various groups in New York, including Kenny Clarke. From 1943 he was a regular player with the Coleman Hawkins sextet, making his recording debut with the band. In fact, Hawkins was one of the first musicians to recognise Monk's unique style. During the 40s Monk worked with Dizzy Gillespie and Cootie Williams and began appearing regularly with his own bands at New York clubs, The Village Vanguard and Mintons, with sidemen such as Sonny Rollins and Art Blakey.

In 1947 Monk made a series of recordings for Alfred Lion at Blue Note Records. The tracks included combinations with bass and drums, horns, and some with Milt Jackson on vibes. These first recordings produced some of Monk's most famous compositions including 'Round Midnight', 'Ruby My Dear' and 'Straight No Chaser'.

In 1951 Monk was wrongly imprisoned for the possession of drugs. Consequently he lost his cabaret card and for the next six years he was unable to gain employment in any of the New York clubs.

However, this did not stop Monk from recording. Between 1952 and 1955 he made a series of recordings for Prestige records. In 1955 the contract was taken over by Riverside Records and Monk recorded Duke Ellington standards to prove that he could play other people's tunes. In 1956 he recorded 'Brilliant Corners' which received favourable reviews and by 1957, when he was able to work again, he appeared at the Five Spot, a fashionable venue for avant-garde music. For this he asked a relatively unknown tenor sax player to play: John Coltrane. It was to become an historic gig.

In 1959, Monk was presented in big band concerts at the Town Hall and other venues and his reputation during the 60s began to blossom. He toured Europe in 1961 and Japan in 1964.

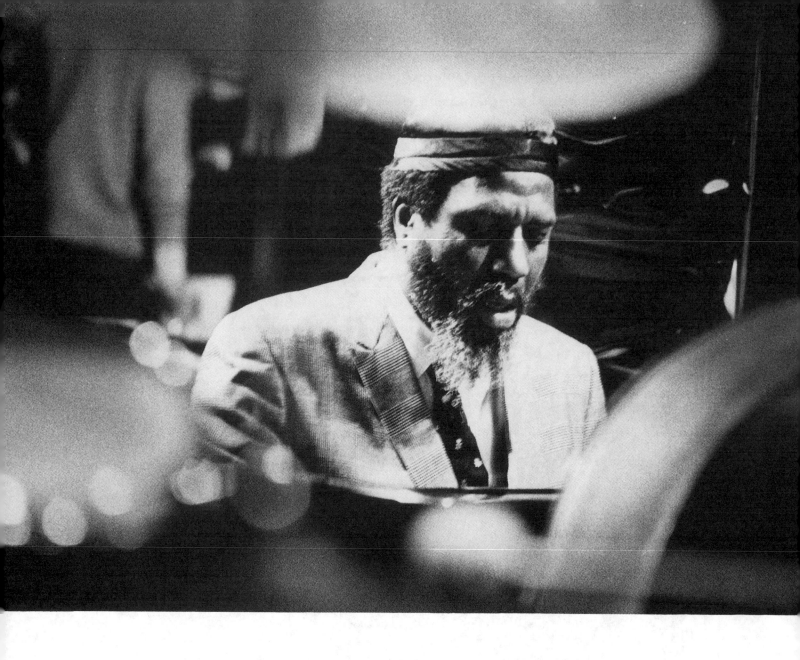

During the late 60s he tended to accept less work but toured widely with the 'Giants of Jazz' in 1971-72. From the mid-70s to his death in 1982 Monk rarely performed in public, due to illness. One of his last appearances was at the Newport Festival in 1974 in a concert of orchestrated arrangements of his compositions.

Although Monk was probably one of the most individual of jazz pianists, he has had very few direct imitators. He has been called the father of the be-bop movement but Monk was never essentially a true be-bop player. Although he was mixing with be-bop players like Parker and Gillespie during the early years, by the mid 1940s Monk was too individualistic to fit into any particular 'school'. After Monk played with Coleman Hawkins in 1943, he developed a 'minimalist' style of playing. Rather than four or five notes in a full chord he would often choose just two notes. Monk achieved the desired effect mainly due to his amazing sensitivity. After 1945, when the 'boppers' were regularly recording and working, Monk was rarely chosen. They preferred to use players like Al Haig and Bud Powell. Essentially, Monk found himself an outsider to the movement he had helped to found.

Unlike most of the be-boppers, Monk did not primarily phrase on the second and fourth beats, and he never felt comfortable with the fast tempos they preferred. Monk's approach to harmony differed. He used just as many altered chords as the boppers did, but instead of using these chromaticisms in the context of a whole chord, for instance by incorporating flattened fifths into a melodic phrase, he kept them naked and open. To many musicians of the 40s this seemed rather perverse.

Although Monk's was a unique way of playing, his appreciation for the earlier piano style of Willie 'the Lion' Smith and Art Tatum is very much in evidence, particularly in his early years.

Monk's compositions have most certainly become jazz 'standards', although the interpretation of 'Round Midnight' is generally misunderstood. It is frequently treated as a sentimental ballad but on hearing the 1947 Blue Note version, one hears it as Monk had intended; menacing and somewhat sombre.

Monk is one of those rare geniuses in jazz. Although he was often ignored by the critics and the general public, he never changed his style, even if this meant being unemployed. Monk's desire to express his own personal ideas in pianistic terms and through his compositions led him to experiment with dissonance in a way that many musicians considered very unusual but strangely attractive. Because Monk is so personal a player, his influence is difficult to assess. Most jazz musicians have listened to Monk and although the influence is not always immediate, it is most certainly there.

blue monk

by Thelonious Monk

Medium swing

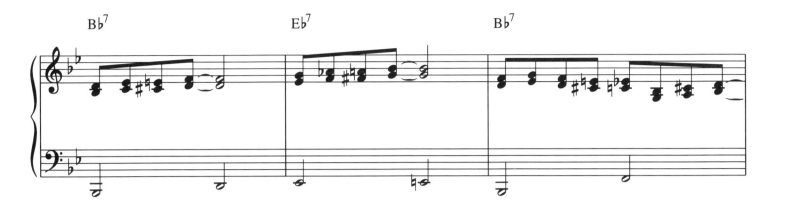

brilliant corners

by Thelonious Monk

Medium tempo

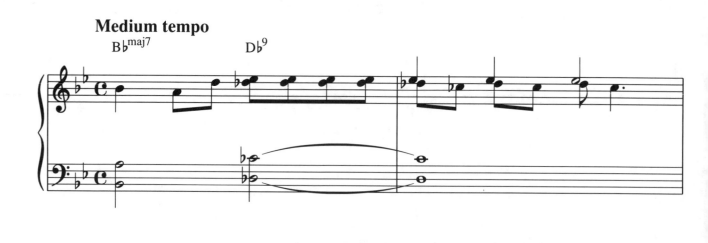

criss cross

by Thelonious Monk

Fast swing tempo

Solo by Lou Donaldson

Solo by Monk

evidence

by Thelonious Monk

Fast swing tempo

D.%. AL CODA

CODA

misterioso

by Thelonious Monk

Slow blues tempo

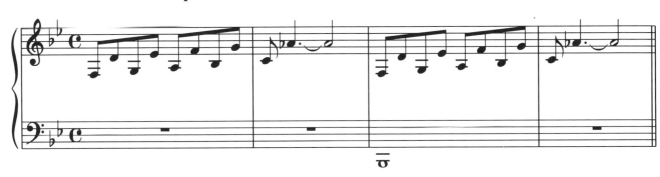

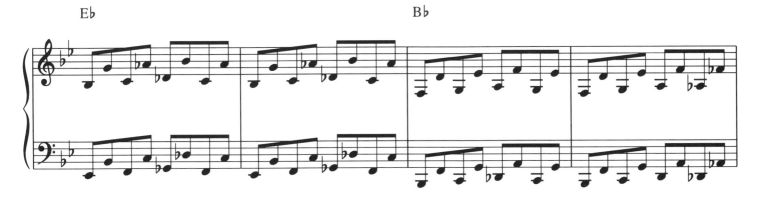

i mean you

by Thelonious Monk & Coleman Hawkins

Medium swing tempo

in walked bud

by Thelonious Monk

Fast bebop

hackensack

by Thelonious Monk

Medium swing tempo

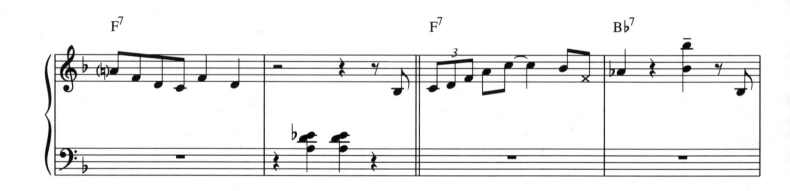

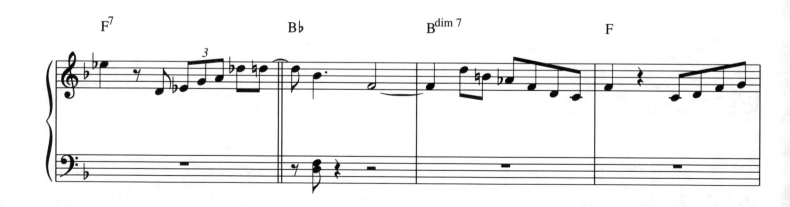

D.𝄋 AL CODA

⊕ CODA

little rootie tootie

by Thelonious Monk

monk's dream

by Thelonious Monk

monk's mood

by Thelonious Monk

rhythm-a-ning

by Thelonious Monk

Fast bebop

nutty

by Thelonious Monk

round midnight

by Cootie Williams & Thelonious Monk

Ballad tempo (not too slow)

pannonica

by Thelonious Monk

Slow ballad tempo

something in blue

by Thelonious Monk

Slow blues tempo

skippy

by Thelonious Monk

Fast bop tempo

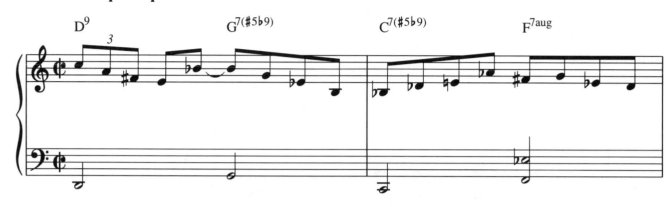

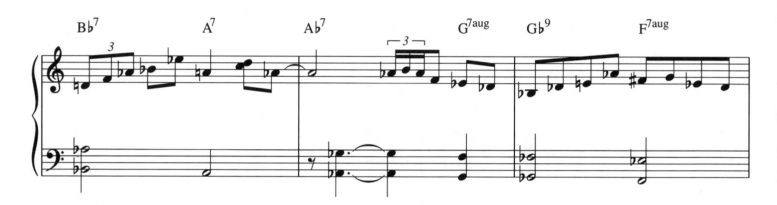

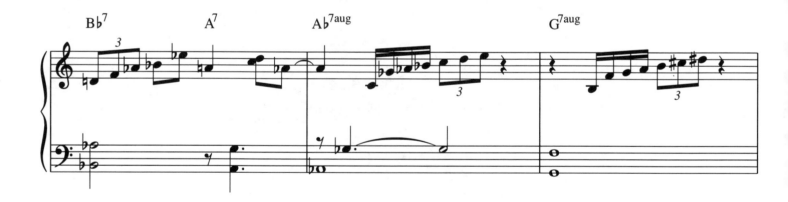

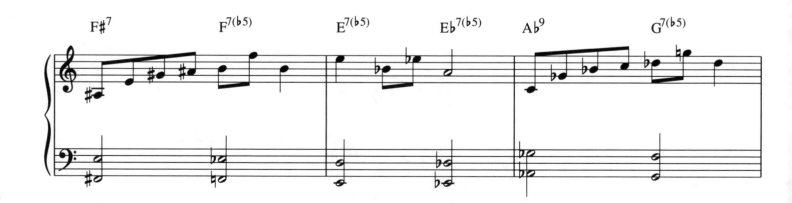

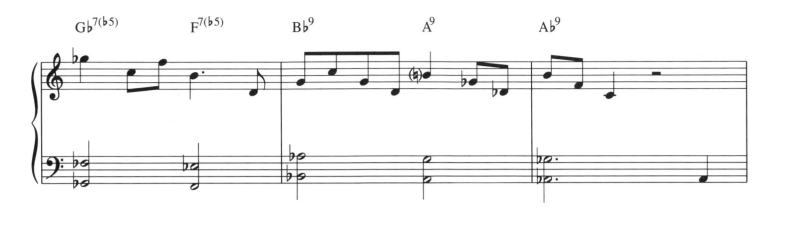

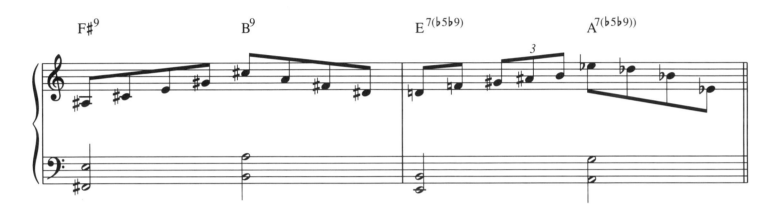

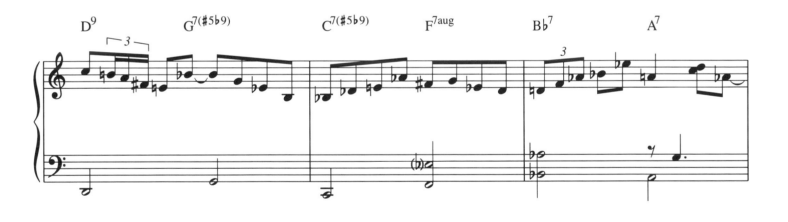

straight no chaser

by Thelonious Monk

Medium swing tempo

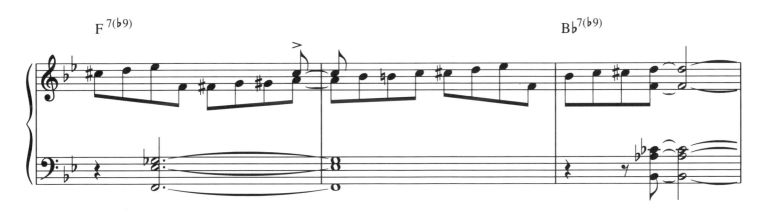

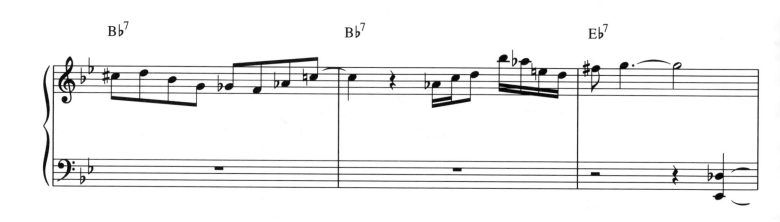

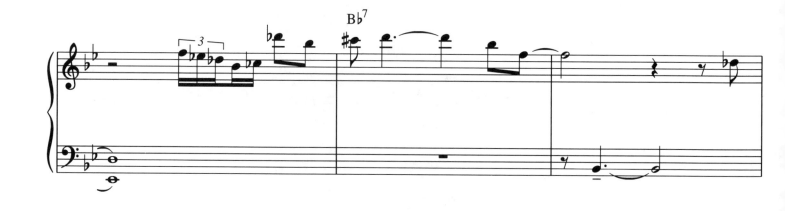

D.𝄋 AL FINE

teo

by Thelonious Monk

Medium swing tempo

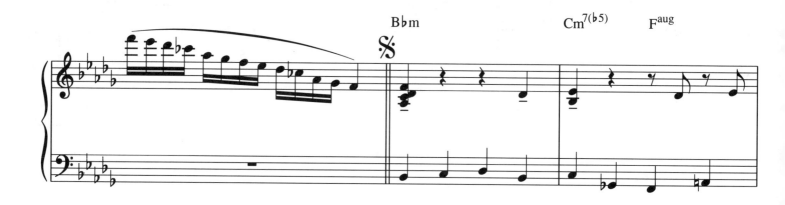

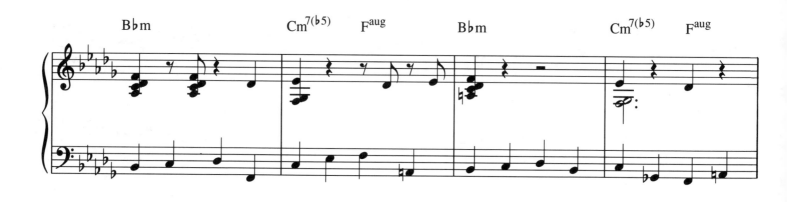

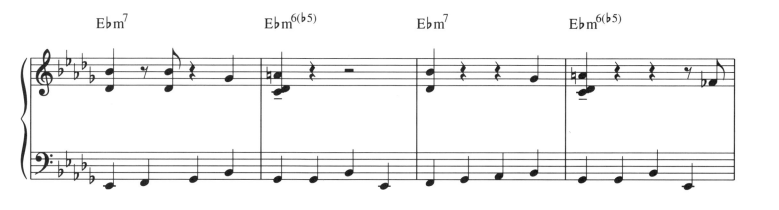

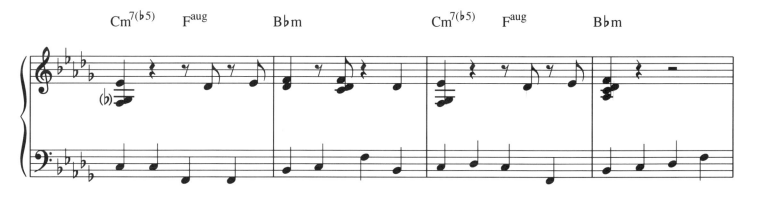

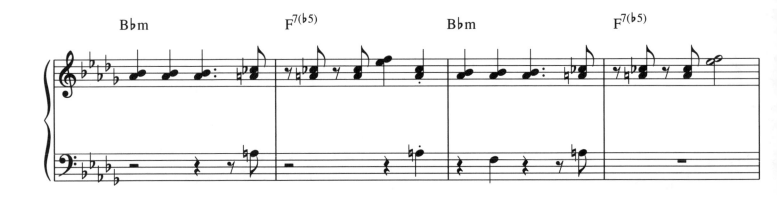

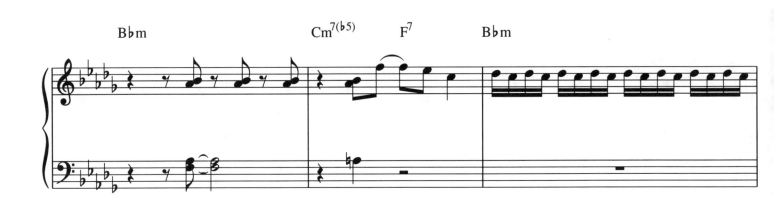

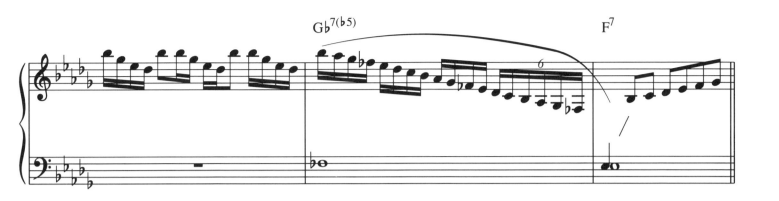

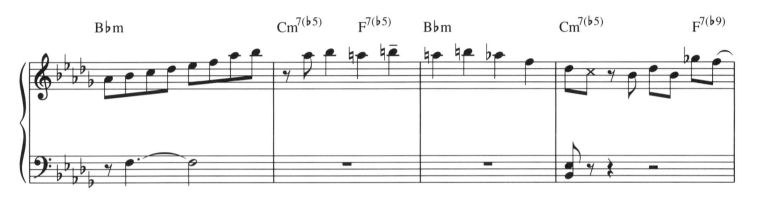

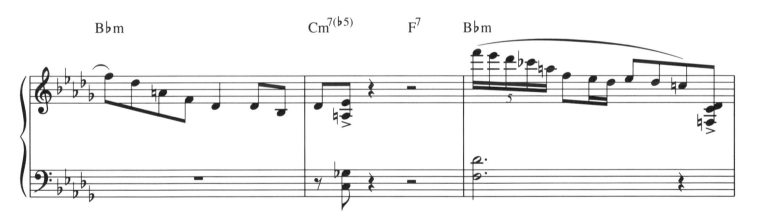

D.𝄋 AL CODA

⊕ CODA

thelonious

by Thelonious Monk

Medium fast swing

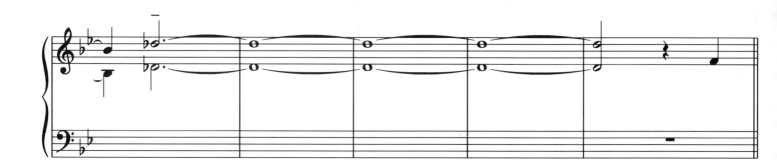

* The descending chordal movement is played by the horns only.

well you needn't

by Thelonious Monk

Medium swing

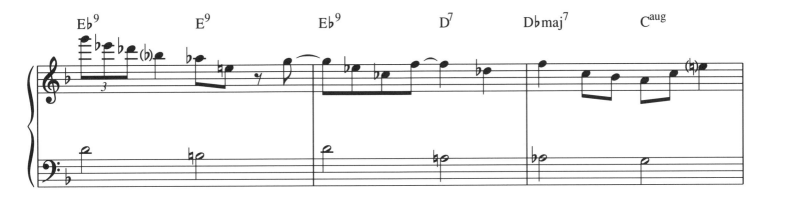

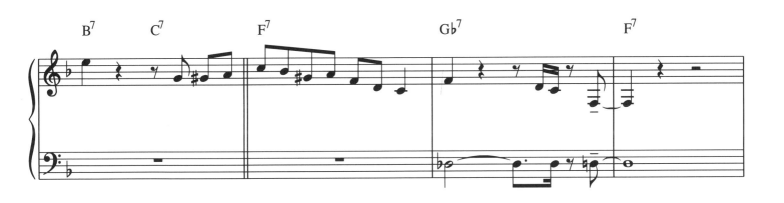

D.𝄋 AL CODA   ⊕ CODA

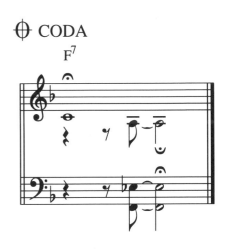

2/06(57747)

selected recordings:

Genius Of Modern Music Vol.1 (Blue Note)

Genius Of Modern Music Vol.2 (Blue Note)

Monk And Coltrane (Riverside)

Something In Blue (Black Lion)

Thelonious Monk: Greatest Hits (Riverside)

Brilliance (Milestone)

Thelonious Monk At Town Hall (Riverside)

Sweets, Lips And Lots Of Jazz (Xanadu)

Thelonious Monk And Sonny Rollins (Jazzland)

Monk Big Band And Quartet In Concert (Columbia)

Pure Monk (Milestone)

Exclusive Distributors:
Music Sales Limited
8/9 Frith Street, London W1V 5TZ, England.
Music Sales Pty Limited
120 Rothschild Avenue, Rosebery, NSW 2018, Australia.

This book © Copyright 1993 by Wise Publications
Order No. AM91078
ISBN 0-7119-3409-6

Unauthorised reproduction of any part of this
publication by any means including photocopying is
an infringement of copyright.

Book design by Michael Bell Design.
Compiled by Peter Evans.
Photographs courtesy of Mick Doyle, Jazz Index.
Music arranged by Steve Hill.
Music processed by New Notations.

Your Guarantee of Quality:
As publishers, we strive to produce every book
to the highest commercial standards.

The music has been freshly engraved and the book
has been carefully designed to minimise awkward page
turns and to make playing from it a real pleasure.

Particular care has been given to specifying acid-free,
neutral-sized paper which has not been chlorine bleached
but produced with special regard for the environment.
Throughout, the printing and binding have been
planned to ensure a sturdy, attractive publication
which should give years of enjoyment.

If your copy fails to meet our high standards, please
inform us and we will gladly replace it.

Music Sales' complete catalogue lists thousands
of titles and is free from your local music shop,
or direct from Music Sales Limited.
Please send a cheque/postal order for £1.50 for
postage to Music Sales Limited, Newmarket Road,
Bury St. Edmunds, Suffolk IP33 3YB.

Printed in the United Kingdom by
Caligraving Limited, Thetford, Norfolk.